The Power of Knowledge:

Inspires Environmenta

Henri Dubois

Title: The Power of Knowledge: How Education Inspires Environmental Stewardship

Author's: Henri Dubois.

This book was printed and published by [Publisher's: Henri Dubois] in [2023]

ISBN:

TABLE OF CONTENTS

Chapter 1: Understanding the Connection between Education and Environmental Stewardship

The Power of Knowledge: Introduction to the book's purpose and objectives

Welcome, students, to the wonderful world of knowledge and education! In this subchapter, we will delve into the purpose and objectives of our book, "The Power of Knowledge: How Education Inspires Environmental Stewardship." As the title suggests, this book aims to highlight the vital role education plays in promoting environmental stewardship.

Education is the key that unlocks countless opportunities and empowers individuals to make a positive impact on the world. It equips us with the knowledge and skills needed to understand complex environmental challenges, encourages critical thinking, and fosters a sense of responsibility towards our planet.

The objective of this book is to demonstrate the importance of education in promoting environmental stewardship. We aim to inspire you, the students, to recognize your role as future environmental stewards and to take action towards building a sustainable future. By sharing compelling stories, research, and practical examples, we hope to ignite your passion for learning and empower you to make a difference.

Throughout the chapters, we will explore various aspects of environmental stewardship, such as climate change, pollution, conservation, and sustainable living. We will dive into the interconnectedness of ecosystems, the impact of human activities on the environment, and the importance of sustainable practices. By understanding the intricate web of life and the consequences of our actions, we can make informed choices that support a healthier planet.

Furthermore, this book will showcase the power of education in addressing environmental challenges. It will highlight the success stories of individuals and communities who have used their knowledge to create positive change. From grassroots movements to global initiatives, we will explore how education has been a catalyst for transformation and inspired people to take action.

By the end of this book, we hope you will not only have a deeper understanding of the importance of education but also feel motivated to embark on your own journey as environmental stewards. Through education, we have the power to shape a more sustainable and equitable future for all.

So, dear students, let us embark on this exciting adventure together. Let us unlock the power of knowledge and harness it to become agents of change. Let us inspire one another, share ideas, and work towards a world where education and environmental stewardship go hand in hand. Get ready to be inspired, informed, and empowered - for the journey of a lifetime awaits!

Exploring the Environmental Crisis: Understanding the urgent need for environmental stewardship

In today's world, it has become increasingly evident that our planet is facing an environmental crisis. From climate change and deforestation to pollution and the depletion of natural resources, the negative impacts of human activities on the environment are undeniable. As students, it is crucial for us to understand the urgent need for environmental stewardship and the role that education plays in inspiring and empowering us to become responsible caretakers of our planet.

Education is the key to unlocking the power of knowledge, and it is through education that we can develop a deep understanding of the importance of environmental stewardship. The more we learn about the interconnectedness of ecosystems, the fragile balance of nature, and the consequences of our actions, the more compelled we become to take action and make a positive difference.

By delving into the environmental crisis, we can grasp the gravity of the situation and recognize that our actions, both individually and collectively, have far-reaching consequences. We will learn about the devastating effects of climate change, such as rising sea levels, extreme weather events, and the loss of biodiversity. We will discover how deforestation leads to habitat destruction for countless species and contributes to global warming. We will understand the detrimental impact of pollution on human health and ecosystems. And we will realize the urgent need to conserve our finite natural resources for future generations.

Education also teaches us about the importance of sustainable practices and alternative solutions. We can explore renewable energy sources like solar and wind power, learn about sustainable agriculture and waste management techniques, and understand the importance of reducing our carbon footprint. Through education, we can gain the knowledge and skills needed to develop innovative and sustainable solutions to the environmental challenges we face.

Furthermore, education equips us with the tools to become advocates for change. Armed with knowledge, we can raise awareness about environmental issues, engage in meaningful discussions, and inspire others to take action. We can become the driving force behind local, national, and global initiatives aimed at protecting the environment, promoting sustainable development, and ensuring a better future for all.

In conclusion, the environmental crisis demands our immediate attention and action. As students, we have the opportunity and responsibility to become informed and engaged environmental stewards. Education is the catalyst that will empower us to understand the urgency of the situation, develop sustainable solutions, and inspire others to join the cause. Let us embrace the power of knowledge and work together to create a more sustainable and environmentally conscious future.

The Role of Education in Environmental Awareness: Discussing the importance of education in addressing environmental challenges

In today's world, where the environment is facing multiple challenges such as climate change, deforestation, and pollution, it is critical for us as students to understand the importance of education in addressing these issues. Education plays a vital role in creating environmental awareness and shaping us into responsible environmental stewards. This subchapter aims to highlight the significance of education in addressing environmental challenges and inspiring us to take action.

Education serves as a powerful tool that equips us with the knowledge and skills needed to understand the complexities of environmental issues. By learning about the environment, its ecosystems, and the interdependence of all living beings, we gain a deeper appreciation for the natural world. Education provides us with the understanding that the choices we make can have a profound impact on the environment, both positive and negative.

Furthermore, education helps us develop critical thinking and problem-solving skills, which are essential for finding innovative solutions to environmental challenges. Through education, we learn how to analyze problems, evaluate different perspectives, and make informed decisions. This empowers us to become active participants in finding sustainable solutions to address environmental degradation.

Education also fosters a sense of responsibility and empathy towards the environment. By learning about the negative consequences of human actions on the planet, we develop a desire to make a positive difference. Education instills in us a sense of environmental stewardship, encouraging us to take actions that protect and preserve the environment for future generations.

Moreover, education provides opportunities for practical experiences and hands-on learning. Field trips, outdoor activities, and environmental projects allow us to connect with nature and witness firsthand the impact of human actions. These experiences deepen our understanding of environmental issues and make the learning process more engaging and memorable.

Lastly, education plays a crucial role in raising awareness and inspiring collective action. By educating ourselves and others, we can create a ripple effect that spreads knowledge and prompts individuals, communities, and even governments to take action. Education empowers us to advocate for policy changes, engage in sustainable practices, and contribute to environmental conservation efforts.

In conclusion, education is an invaluable tool in addressing environmental challenges. It provides us with the knowledge, skills, and motivation to become responsible environmental stewards. By understanding the importance of education in environmental awareness, we can actively contribute to creating a sustainable future for ourselves and future generations. Let us embrace the power of education and work together to inspire environmental stewardship.

Chapter 2: The Benefits of Environmental Education for Students

Developing an Environmental Ethic: How education shapes personal values and attitudes towards the environment

Education is a powerful tool that has the potential to inspire and shape individuals' values and attitudes towards the environment. In today's world, where environmental challenges are becoming increasingly pressing, it is essential for students to understand the importance of education in fostering an environmental ethic. This subchapter delves into the transformative power of education and its role in inspiring environmental stewardship.

Education serves as a catalyst for change, offering knowledge and understanding about the environment and its interconnectedness with human life. Through educational institutions and initiatives, students gain a comprehensive understanding of the complexities and challenges facing our planet. By exploring topics such as climate change, biodiversity loss, and pollution, students become aware of the urgent need for environmental preservation.

Moreover, education shapes personal values by instilling a sense of responsibility and empathy towards the environment. It teaches students about the delicate balance between human needs and the natural world, encouraging them to make sustainable choices. By learning about the impacts of individual actions on the environment, students are empowered to make conscious decisions that prioritize the well-being of the planet.

Education also cultivates critical thinking skills, enabling students to analyze environmental issues from multiple perspectives. It encourages them to question existing systems and seek innovative solutions to environmental challenges. By fostering creativity and problem-solving abilities, education equips students with the tools to become environmental stewards and advocates for change.

Furthermore, education provides opportunities for hands-on experiences and practical learning, which are crucial for developing an environmental ethic. Field trips, environmental clubs, and community service projects allow students to engage directly with the environment, fostering a deep connection and appreciation for nature. These experiences not only enhance students' understanding of environmental issues but also inspire a sense of responsibility to protect and conserve the natural world.

In conclusion, education plays a fundamental role in shaping personal values and attitudes towards the environment. By providing knowledge, fostering critical thinking, and facilitating hands-on experiences, education inspires students to become environmental stewards. As students, embracing the importance of education in developing an environmental ethic will empower us to create a sustainable future for generations to come.

Empowering Future Leaders: The role of education in nurturing young environmental advocates

In today's rapidly changing world, it has become increasingly important to address the environmental challenges that our planet faces. As students, you have a unique opportunity to make a significant impact on the future of our environment. Education plays a vital role in nurturing young environmental advocates and empowering you to become the leaders of tomorrow.

Education is the key to understanding the importance of environmental stewardship. It provides you with the knowledge and tools necessary to comprehend the complexities of our planet and the delicate balance that exists within its ecosystems. Through education, you gain a deeper understanding of the interconnectedness of all living beings and the impact our actions have on the environment.

By educating yourself about environmental issues, you are equipped with the necessary skills to become effective advocates for change. Education enables you to critically analyze environmental problems, evaluate potential solutions, and communicate your ideas effectively. It empowers you to take action and make informed decisions that contribute to the preservation of our natural resources.

Furthermore, education fosters a sense of responsibility and stewardship towards the environment. It instills in you a deep appreciation for the beauty and value of our natural world. Through education, you develop a sense of empathy towards all living beings and understand the importance of preserving biodiversity. Education empowers you to become environmental ambassadors, spreading awareness and inspiring others to take action.

Moreover, education provides you with the opportunity to develop essential skills such as critical thinking, problem-solving, and collaboration. These skills are invaluable in addressing complex environmental issues that require innovative solutions. Education equips you with the tools needed to navigate challenges, find creative solutions, and collaborate with others to create a sustainable future.

In conclusion, the role of education in nurturing young environmental advocates cannot be overstated. It is through education that you gain the knowledge, skills, and sense of responsibility needed to become effective leaders in environmental stewardship. By empowering yourself with education, you have the power to make a positive impact on our planet and create a sustainable future for generations to come.

Building Sustainable Communities: How education contributes to the creation of environmentally conscious societies

Introduction:
In today's world, where environmental issues are becoming increasingly prevalent, it is imperative that we develop a deep understanding of the importance of education in creating environmentally conscious societies. Education plays a vital role in shaping our perceptions, behaviors, and actions towards the environment. This subchapter explores how education contributes to building sustainable communities and why it is crucial for students to embrace the power of education in becoming environmental stewards.

Education as a Catalyst for Change:
Education serves as a catalyst for change by equipping individuals with the knowledge and skills needed to understand and address environmental challenges. Through formal education systems, students gain a comprehensive understanding of the interconnectedness between human actions and the environment. They learn about ecological systems, climate change, resource management, and sustainable practices. By acquiring this knowledge, students become empowered to make informed decisions and take actions that contribute to the preservation of the environment.

Fostering a Sense of Responsibility:
Education instills a sense of responsibility in individuals towards their communities and the environment. Through educational programs and initiatives, students are encouraged to develop empathy and care for the natural world. They learn about the impacts of human activities on the environment and the consequences of unsustainable practices.

As students gain a deeper understanding of these issues, they are more likely to adopt environmentally conscious behaviors and actively participate in creating sustainable communities.

Creating Future Environmental Stewards:
Education plays a vital role in nurturing the next generation of environmental stewards. By incorporating environmental education into the curriculum, students are exposed to hands-on experiences that foster a connection with nature. Field trips, outdoor learning, and environmental clubs provide platforms for students to engage in practical activities that promote sustainability. Moreover, education helps students develop critical thinking skills, enabling them to analyze complex environmental issues and propose innovative solutions.

Conclusion:
Education is a powerful tool that can inspire environmental stewardship and contribute to the creation of sustainable communities. By equipping students with knowledge, fostering a sense of responsibility, and nurturing environmental stewards, education plays a pivotal role in shaping the future of our planet. As students, it is crucial to recognize the importance of education in our journey towards becoming environmentally conscious individuals. By embracing the power of education, we can collectively work towards building a more sustainable and environmentally friendly world for generations to come.

Chapter 3: Education as a Tool for Environmental Conservation

Environmental Science Education: Fostering scientific knowledge and critical thinking skills

In today's rapidly changing world, the importance of education cannot be overstated. With the ever-increasing threats to our environment and the urgent need for sustainable solutions, it has become crucial to equip students with the necessary knowledge and critical thinking skills to tackle these challenges. Environmental science education plays a vital role in fostering scientific knowledge and critical thinking skills, enabling students to become informed and responsible global citizens.

Environmental science education goes beyond simply learning about the natural world. It provides students with a comprehensive understanding of the interconnections between human activities and the environment. By studying topics such as climate change, biodiversity loss, pollution, and resource depletion, students gain insight into the complex issues affecting our planet. This knowledge empowers them to make informed decisions and take action to protect and conserve our natural resources.

Moreover, environmental science education cultivates critical thinking skills. Students are encouraged to analyze and evaluate scientific data, understand cause-and-effect relationships, and develop solutions to environmental problems. They learn to question prevailing assumptions and seek evidence-based answers, honing their ability to think critically and make informed judgments.

In a world where misinformation and fake news are prevalent, the ability to think critically is more important than ever. Environmental science education equips students with the skills to discern fact from fiction, making them less susceptible to manipulation and misinformation. By developing critical thinking skills, students become better equipped to navigate complex environmental issues and contribute to evidence-based decision-making processes.

Furthermore, environmental science education fosters a sense of environmental stewardship. By understanding the impact of their actions on the environment, students develop a deep appreciation for the natural world and a sense of responsibility towards its preservation. They are encouraged to think globally and act locally, finding practical ways to make a positive difference in their own communities.

In conclusion, environmental science education is crucial in today's rapidly changing world. By fostering scientific knowledge and critical thinking skills, it empowers students to become informed and responsible global citizens. It equips them with the tools to understand complex environmental issues, make informed decisions, and contribute to sustainable solutions. Environmental science education not only inspires a love for the natural world but also instills a sense of responsibility towards its protection and preservation.

Environmental Literacy: Understanding the interconnectedness of environmental issues

In today's rapidly changing world, the importance of education cannot be overstated. As students, you have the incredible opportunity to gain knowledge and understanding that will empower you to become environmental stewards and make a positive difference in the world.

One crucial aspect of environmental education is developing environmental literacy. Environmental literacy goes beyond simply knowing facts about the environment; it involves understanding the interconnectedness of environmental issues and the impacts they have on our planet and society as a whole.

To be environmentally literate means recognizing that everything in our world is connected. It means understanding that actions taken in one part of the world can have far-reaching consequences in another. For example, the burning of fossil fuels in one country contributes to climate change, which affects weather patterns and ecosystems worldwide. By grasping these connections, you can see the bigger picture and make informed decisions that consider the long-term consequences of your actions.

Environmental literacy helps you understand the intricate web of relationships between humans, nature, and the environment. It enables you to comprehend how our daily choices, such as food consumption, energy use, and transportation, impact natural resources, biodiversity, and the overall health of our planet. Armed with this knowledge, you can make informed decisions that minimize your ecological footprint and promote sustainability.

Moreover, understanding the interconnectedness of environmental issues allows you to appreciate the complexity and urgency of environmental challenges. Climate change, deforestation, pollution, and species extinction are not isolated problems; they are interconnected and exacerbate one another. By recognizing these connections, you can advocate for holistic solutions that address multiple issues simultaneously.

Environmental literacy also equips you with the skills to analyze and evaluate information critically. In an era of misinformation and greenwashing, it is vital to be able to discern accurate and reliable information from misleading claims. This ability empowers you to make well-informed decisions and take action based on scientific evidence and sound reasoning.

Ultimately, developing environmental literacy is key to inspiring environmental stewardship. It fosters a sense of responsibility and empowers you to take action to protect and preserve our planet for future generations. By understanding the interconnectedness of environmental issues, you can become informed advocates and catalysts for change in your communities and beyond.

In conclusion, education plays a pivotal role in inspiring environmental stewardship. By developing environmental literacy and understanding the interconnectedness of environmental issues, you can become informed, empowered, and active agents of change. Embrace the power of knowledge and join the global movement towards a sustainable and thriving future.

Environmental Education in Practice: Showcasing successful initiatives and programs

As students, we often wonder how we can make a real impact on the world around us. We recognize the urgent need to protect our environment and create a sustainable future, but we may not always know where to start. This subchapter, "Environmental Education in Practice: Showcasing Successful Initiatives and Programs," aims to inspire and guide students like us to take action through education.

Education is a powerful tool that can ignite our passion for environmental stewardship. By learning about the importance of education in the context of environmental issues, we can understand how knowledge empowers us to make a difference. This subchapter will highlight successful initiatives and programs that have effectively incorporated environmental education into their practices.

One such initiative is the Earth Guardians program, which empowers young people to become environmental leaders in their communities. Through a combination of education, mentorship, and action, Earth Guardians has created a network of passionate individuals dedicated to addressing climate change and advocating for environmental justice.

Another successful program is the Children's Forest, a collaborative effort between schools and environmental organizations. By providing students with hands-on learning experiences in nearby forests, this program fosters a deep connection to nature and encourages responsible environmental practices.

The subchapter will also delve into the role of schools in promoting environmental education. It will showcase schools that have integrated sustainability into their curriculum, teaching students about environmental issues and inspiring them to take action. These schools serve as examples of how education can be transformative, not only for individual students but also for entire communities.

Furthermore, we will explore the importance of outdoor education and experiential learning. Initiatives like outdoor classrooms, nature-based field trips, and community gardens offer students the opportunity to engage directly with the environment, fostering a sense of wonder and responsibility.

By showcasing these successful initiatives and programs, this subchapter will inspire students to recognize the power of education in promoting environmental stewardship. It will provide practical examples and ideas for how we can get involved, whether through joining existing programs or starting our own initiatives. Ultimately, it will empower us to become active participants in creating a sustainable future for ourselves and future generations.

In conclusion, this subchapter highlights the importance of education in inspiring environmental stewardship. By showcasing successful initiatives and programs, it aims to motivate students to take action and make a positive impact on the environment. Through education, we can become the next generation of environmental leaders, equipped with the knowledge and passion to create a sustainable future.

Chapter 4: Integrating Environmental Education into the Curriculum

Incorporating Environmental Themes in Various Subjects: Exploring opportunities in science, social studies, and language arts

Education plays a pivotal role in shaping the minds of individuals and preparing them for a sustainable future. As students, it is crucial to understand the importance of education, not only for personal growth but also for the greater good of our planet. In this subchapter, we will delve into the ways in which environmental themes can be integrated into different subjects like science, social studies, and language arts, enriching our educational experience and fostering environmental stewardship.

Science, as a subject, provides us with a deeper understanding of the natural world around us. By incorporating environmental themes, such as climate change, pollution, and biodiversity, we can develop a strong foundation in scientific knowledge while simultaneously cultivating a sense of responsibility towards the environment. Through experiments, field trips, and research projects, we can explore the impact of human activities on ecosystems and discover innovative solutions to address environmental challenges.

In social studies, we can explore the interconnectedness between societies, cultures, and the environment. By studying topics like sustainable development, environmental justice, and resource management, we can gain insights into the global environmental issues that affect our world. This interdisciplinary approach helps us recognize the importance of collective action and empowers us to advocate for change at local, national, and international levels.

Language arts, on the other hand, allows us to express our thoughts and emotions through various mediums like writing, reading, and storytelling. By incorporating environmental themes into literature, poetry, and creative writing, we can develop a deep appreciation for nature and foster empathy towards all living beings. Through analyzing environmental texts and engaging in discussions, we can sharpen our critical thinking skills and become effective communicators, inspiring others to take action for a sustainable future.

By integrating environmental themes into these subjects, we not only enhance our knowledge but also develop essential skills such as problem-solving, collaboration, and critical thinking. These skills are crucial for addressing the complex environmental challenges we face today and becoming responsible stewards of our planet. As students, we have the power to make a difference, and education equips us with the tools to create a sustainable and thriving world for future generations.

In conclusion, incorporating environmental themes in science, social studies, and language arts provides us with a holistic approach to education. It enables us to develop a deep understanding of environmental issues, cultivates empathy and responsibility, and equips us with the skills necessary to tackle the complex challenges of the 21st century. By embracing these opportunities, we can become informed global citizens and inspire others to join us in the quest for environmental stewardship. Education truly holds the power to shape our future and create a sustainable world that we can all be proud of.

Environmental Education Beyond the Classroom: Emphasizing the value of field trips, outdoor learning, and hands-on experiences

In today's era, the importance of education cannot be understated. It serves as a powerful tool that empowers individuals with knowledge and skills, while also inspiring them to become responsible stewards of the environment. As students, you hold the key to a sustainable future, and it is through environmental education that you can unlock your potential to make a positive impact on the world around you.

While classroom learning is crucial, it is equally important to explore the world beyond the four walls of your school. Field trips, outdoor learning activities, and hands-on experiences offer invaluable opportunities to connect with nature, deepen your understanding of environmental issues, and cultivate a sense of appreciation for the natural world.

Field trips, for instance, provide a unique chance to witness firsthand the beauty and complexity of ecosystems. Whether visiting a local park, a nature reserve, or even a recycling facility, these experiences allow you to see how the concepts you learn in class are applied in real-life scenarios. By immersing yourself in nature, you can develop a profound connection with the environment, fostering a sense of responsibility towards its conservation.

Outdoor learning activities, such as nature walks, tree planting, or even gardening, offer hands-on experiences that stimulate curiosity and foster a deeper appreciation for the environment. These activities allow you to engage with the natural world, fostering a sense of wonder and awe. By exploring the outdoors, you can observe the intricate relationships between living organisms, learn about the importance of biodiversity, and witness the impact of human activities on ecosystems.

Moreover, hands-on experiences, such as science experiments or environmental projects, provide an opportunity to apply your knowledge and skills in a practical setting. These activities encourage critical thinking, problem-solving, and creativity, while also instilling a sense of ownership and responsibility for the environment. By actively participating in projects that aim to address environmental challenges, you can become agents of change and contribute to the development of sustainable solutions.

In conclusion, while classroom education is vital, environmental education beyond the classroom is equally essential. Field trips, outdoor learning activities, and hands-on experiences offer students the chance to connect with nature, deepen their understanding of environmental issues, and inspire them to become responsible stewards of the environment. By embracing these opportunities, you can unlock your potential to make a positive impact on the world, creating a sustainable future for generations to come. Remember, the power of education lies in your hands, and it is through your knowledge and actions that you can inspire environmental stewardship and shape a better world.

Collaborative Approaches: Engaging students, educators, and the community in environmental education efforts

In today's world, where environmental issues have become increasingly pressing, it is crucial to engage students, educators, and the community in environmental education efforts. By working together collaboratively, we can foster a deep understanding of the importance of education in inspiring environmental stewardship.

Education is the key to unlocking a sustainable future. It empowers individuals with knowledge and skills to make informed decisions, take responsible actions, and lead change. Environmental education, in particular, equips students with the understanding of environmental challenges, their causes, and potential solutions. It encourages critical thinking, problem-solving, and the ability to make sustainable choices in their everyday lives.

Collaborative approaches play a vital role in enhancing the effectiveness of environmental education efforts. By bringing together students, educators, and the community, we can create a network of support and resources that enriches the learning experience. This collaboration allows for a holistic approach to education, where various perspectives and expertise contribute to a well-rounded understanding of environmental issues.

Engaging students in environmental education efforts is essential to instill a sense of responsibility and stewardship towards the environment. By actively involving them in hands-on activities, field trips, and community projects, they can witness the real-world impact of their actions. Working alongside educators and the community, students can develop a deep connection with nature and understand the interconnectedness of environmental systems.

Educators, on the other hand, play a crucial role in facilitating environmental education. They possess the knowledge and skills to effectively communicate complex concepts, inspire curiosity, and guide students towards a deeper understanding of environmental issues. By collaborating with other educators and community organizations, they can access a wealth of resources, expertise, and innovative teaching methods that enhance their teaching practices.

The involvement of the community is equally important in environmental education efforts. The community provides a rich source of knowledge, experiences, and support that can enrich the educational journey. By engaging community members in environmental initiatives, students can witness the positive impact of collective action and develop a sense of belonging and responsibility towards their local environment.

In conclusion, collaborative approaches are key to engaging students, educators, and the community in environmental education efforts. By working together, we can create a transformative learning experience that inspires environmental stewardship. Education empowers individuals, and when combined with collaborative efforts, it becomes a powerful tool to address environmental challenges and create a sustainable future for generations to come.

Chapter 5: Overcoming Challenges in Environmental Education

Limited Resources: Strategies for promoting environmental education in resource-constrained settings

In today's world, where environmental challenges are becoming increasingly urgent, the importance of education cannot be overstated. Education is a powerful tool that not only imparts knowledge but also inspires environmental stewardship. However, in resource-constrained settings, promoting environmental education can be a daunting task. This subchapter explores strategies for overcoming limited resources and making a significant impact on environmental education.

1. Partnerships and Collaborations: One of the most effective strategies in resource-constrained settings is to establish partnerships and collaborations with local organizations, NGOs, and government agencies. By pooling resources and expertise, you can create a more comprehensive and impactful environmental education program.

2. Utilize Existing Infrastructure: In resource-constrained settings, it is crucial to utilize existing infrastructure such as schools, community centers, and libraries. These spaces can be transformed into hubs for environmental education by incorporating relevant materials, resources, and activities.

3. Mobile Education Units: In areas where resources are limited, consider implementing mobile education units. These mobile units can visit different communities, providing hands-on environmental

education experiences through interactive workshops, games, and exhibits.

4. Localize the Curriculum: Tailoring the environmental education curriculum to the local context is essential. By incorporating local environmental issues, traditional knowledge, and practices, students can develop a deeper understanding of their surroundings and become more engaged in environmental stewardship.

5. Engaging Local Leaders and Influencers: In resource-constrained settings, local leaders and influencers play a vital role in shaping community attitudes and behaviors. Engaging them in environmental education initiatives can amplify the impact and encourage community-wide participation.

6. Utilize Technology: Technology can bridge the gap in resource-constrained settings by providing access to educational resources and tools. Online platforms, video conferences, and e-learning modules can help overcome physical limitations and reach a wider audience.

7. Community Participation: Encouraging community participation is crucial for the success of environmental education initiatives. By involving students, parents, and community members in planning and implementing programs, a sense of ownership and responsibility is fostered, ensuring long-term sustainability.

In resource-constrained settings, the importance of education in fostering environmental stewardship becomes even more critical. By employing these strategies, educators, students, and community members can overcome limitations and make a significant impact on environmental education. Together, we can inspire a new generation of environmental stewards who are equipped with the knowledge and passion to safeguard our planet for future generations.

Engaging Disinterested Students: Techniques for capturing the attention and interest of students not initially inclined towards environmental issues

In today's fast-paced world, where technology dominates our attention, it can be challenging to engage students who may not initially be inclined towards environmental issues. However, the importance of education in inspiring environmental stewardship cannot be overstated. In this subchapter, we explore various techniques that can capture the attention and interest of disinterested students, ultimately inspiring them to become active participants in creating a sustainable future.

1. Make it relevant: Environmental issues may seem distant to some students, so it is crucial to connect the concepts to their daily lives. Highlight how environmental degradation affects their health, well-being, and future prospects. By making it personal, students are more likely to engage and take action.

2. Hands-on experiences: Provide students with real-world experiences that allow them to interact with nature and witness the impact of their actions. Field trips, hands-on experiments, and community service projects can bring environmental issues to life and foster a sense of responsibility.

3. Use technology wisely: Technology can be both a distraction and a powerful tool for engagement. Utilize interactive apps, virtual reality experiences, and online platforms to create immersive and engaging learning experiences. By harnessing technology, we can bridge the gap between disinterested students and environmental issues.

4. Storytelling: Humans are wired to connect with stories. Use narratives that showcase the positive impact of environmental stewardship and the consequences of inaction. By weaving stories into your teaching, you can captivate students' attention and inspire them to take action.

5. Collaborative learning: Foster a sense of community and teamwork by encouraging students to work together on environmental projects. Assign group projects that require critical thinking, problem-solving, and creativity. By working together, students can learn from one another and create a supportive environment where everyone feels engaged and motivated.

6. Gamification: Incorporate elements of gamification into environmental education. Create challenges, competitions, and rewards for achieving sustainability goals. By turning learning into a game, students become more motivated to participate and actively learn about environmental concepts.

Remember, the power of education lies in its ability to inspire and transform. By implementing these techniques, we can ignite a passion for environmental stewardship in even the most disinterested students. Let us empower ourselves with knowledge and work together to create a sustainable future for generations to come.

Overcoming Resistance: Addressing potential barriers and opposition to environmental education initiatives

Introduction:

In our journey towards environmental stewardship, education plays a vital role in shaping our understanding and inspiring positive action. However, as with any transformative initiative, there may be potential barriers and opposition that we need to address. In this subchapter, we will explore some common challenges faced by environmental education initiatives and discuss effective strategies to overcome resistance.

1. Lack of Awareness and Understanding:
One major barrier to environmental education is the lack of awareness and understanding among students and the wider community about the importance of environmental issues. Many may be unfamiliar with the ecological consequences of their actions or unaware of the potential for positive change. To address this, educational institutions should prioritize spreading awareness through engaging campaigns, workshops, and interactive initiatives. By showcasing the direct relevance of environmental education to our daily lives, we can overcome resistance and foster a sense of responsibility towards our environment.

2. Political and Economic Interests:
Another significant challenge faced by environmental education initiatives is opposition from powerful entities with vested interests. Political and economic forces may resist efforts to instill environmental values, fearing potential restrictions or a shift in the status quo. Overcoming this resistance requires a well-informed and

empowered student body, capable of questioning the motives behind such opposition. By highlighting the long-term benefits of environmental stewardship, students can articulate their concerns and advocate for change through peaceful means, such as organizing awareness campaigns, petitions, or engaging in constructive dialogues with policymakers.

3. Cultural and Societal Norms:
Cultural and societal norms can also act as barriers to effective environmental education. Traditional beliefs, consumerism, and a lack of prioritization of environmental issues may hinder efforts to promote sustainable practices. To overcome this resistance, it is crucial to incorporate cultural sensitivity and inclusivity into educational programs. By emphasizing the compatibility of environmental values with cultural heritage, we can encourage students to embrace sustainable practices while respecting diverse perspectives.

4. Limited Resources and Infrastructure:
Insufficient resources and infrastructure can impede the implementation of comprehensive environmental education initiatives. Lack of funding, outdated curricula, and inadequate access to educational materials can hinder progress. Addressing this challenge requires collaborative efforts between educational institutions, local communities, and policymakers. By advocating for increased funding, curriculum updates, and the integration of technology, we can overcome these barriers and ensure access to quality environmental education for all students.

Conclusion:
As we recognize the importance of education in inspiring

environmental stewardship, it is essential to address potential barriers and opposition. By spreading awareness, engaging in peaceful advocacy, promoting cultural sensitivity, and advocating for resources, we can overcome resistance and pave the way for a sustainable future. Together, we can harness the power of knowledge to create a generation of environmentally conscious citizens ready to protect and preserve our planet.

Chapter 6: Inspiring Environmental Stewardship through Education

Providing Role Models and Inspirational Stories: Highlighting individuals who have made a significant impact in environmental conservation

Education is a powerful tool that not only equips us with knowledge but also inspires us to become better stewards of the environment. Throughout history, there have been individuals who have made a significant impact in environmental conservation, serving as role models and sources of inspiration for future generations. In this subchapter, we will explore the stories of these remarkable individuals and their contributions to safeguarding our planet.

One such inspirational figure is Rachel Carson, a marine biologist and nature writer who dedicated her life to raising awareness about the detrimental effects of pesticides on the environment. Through her groundbreaking book, "Silent Spring," Carson shed light on the devastating impact of pesticide use on wildlife and the delicate balance of ecosystems. Her work led to a ban on the pesticide DDT and laid the foundation for the modern environmental movement.

Another notable role model is Wangari Maathai, an environmental and political activist from Kenya. Maathai founded the Green Belt Movement, an organization that focused on reforestation, conservation, and women's rights. By mobilizing communities to plant trees, Maathai not only helped restore degraded lands but also empowered women by providing them with a source of income and promoting sustainable livelihoods.

In addition to these extraordinary individuals, there are countless others who have dedicated their lives to environmental conservation. From indigenous leaders fighting for the protection of their ancestral lands to scientists developing innovative solutions to combat climate change, each person's story highlights the importance of education in driving positive change.

By showcasing these role models and inspirational stories, we aim to inspire students to become environmental stewards themselves. Through education, we can learn from the successes and challenges faced by these individuals, gaining a deeper understanding of the interconnectedness between humans and the natural world.

Furthermore, these stories serve as a reminder that anyone, regardless of their background, can make a difference. By sharing the stories of these remarkable individuals, we hope to instill a sense of empowerment and encourage students to use their education and knowledge to tackle environmental issues in their own communities.

In conclusion, providing role models and sharing inspirational stories is crucial in emphasizing the importance of education in environmental conservation. By highlighting the incredible achievements of individuals like Rachel Carson and Wangari Maathai, we hope to inspire students to become active participants in protecting and preserving our planet for future generations.

Encouraging Student-Led Initiatives: Empowering students to take action and create positive change in their communities

Education plays a crucial role in shaping individuals into responsible and engaged citizens. As students, you have the power to make a difference in your communities, and it is essential to harness this potential to create positive change. This subchapter explores the importance of education in empowering you to take action through student-led initiatives.

Education provides you with the knowledge and skills needed to understand the challenges your community faces, especially in relation to environmental stewardship. By learning about the impact of human activities on the environment, you can develop a sense of responsibility towards preserving and protecting our planet. Education equips you with the tools to analyze complex issues, think critically, and find innovative solutions.

One of the most effective ways to create change is through student-led initiatives. These initiatives empower you to take ownership of the issues you care about and develop practical solutions. By organizing events, campaigns, or projects, you can raise awareness, inspire others, and mobilize your community towards a common goal.

Student-led initiatives also provide an opportunity for personal growth and development. They allow you to develop leadership skills, enhance your communication abilities, and foster collaboration. Engaging in such initiatives not only benefits your community but also helps you build a strong foundation for your future endeavors.

To successfully implement student-led initiatives, it is crucial to identify the areas you are passionate about. Reflect on the issues that resonate with you and align with your values. Whether it's reducing plastic waste, promoting renewable energy, or advocating for sustainable agriculture, choose a cause that ignites your passion and inspires you to take action.

Collaboration is key to the success of any student-led initiative. Seek like-minded individuals, form a team, and work together towards your shared goals. By pooling your resources, skills, and ideas, you can create a more significant impact and inspire others to join your cause.

Remember, change starts with you. With the power of knowledge gained through education, you have the ability to make a difference. Be proactive, take initiative, and never underestimate the influence you can have on your community. By encouraging student-led initiatives, we can empower future generations to become environmental stewards and create a sustainable and thriving world for all.

Collaborating for a Sustainable Future: Promoting partnerships between educational institutions, environmental organizations, and government agencies

In today's world, where the consequences of environmental degradation are becoming increasingly apparent, the need for sustainable practices has never been more urgent. As students, you hold the key to a future that is environmentally sustainable and socially just. Education plays a pivotal role in empowering individuals to become environmental stewards, and it is through collaboration between educational institutions, environmental organizations, and government agencies that we can create a sustainable future.

Education is the foundation upon which environmental stewardship is built. By equipping students with knowledge about the environment and the challenges it faces, educational institutions lay the groundwork for future generations to become environmentally conscious citizens. However, education cannot exist in a vacuum. It is vital for educational institutions to collaborate with environmental organizations and government agencies to provide students with practical experiences and real-world applications of their learning.

Partnerships between educational institutions, environmental organizations, and government agencies offer a myriad of benefits. Environmental organizations bring expertise, resources, and on-the-ground experience to the table. They can offer internships, field trips, and workshops that provide students with hands-on opportunities to engage with environmental issues. By working with government agencies, educational institutions can ensure that their curriculum aligns with current environmental policies and regulations. These collaborations also provide a platform for students to engage in advocacy work and contribute to policy-making processes.

The importance of education in promoting environmental stewardship cannot be overstated. It is through education that students gain the knowledge, skills, and values necessary to become responsible and informed citizens. By collaborating with environmental organizations and government agencies, educational institutions can enhance the educational experience, providing students with a holistic understanding of environmental issues and the tools to address them.

Furthermore, partnerships between these entities foster a sense of community and shared responsibility. Environmental organizations and government agencies can benefit from the fresh ideas and enthusiasm that students bring. By involving students in collaborative projects, these organizations can tap into a new generation of environmental leaders and innovators.

In conclusion, collaboration between educational institutions, environmental organizations, and government agencies is essential for promoting a sustainable future. By working together, we can ensure that education inspires environmental stewardship and equips students with the knowledge and skills necessary to address pressing environmental challenges. As students, you have the power to make a difference. Through education and collaboration, we can create a future that is environmentally sustainable and socially just.

Chapter 7: The Future of Environmental Education

Innovations in Environmental Education: Exploring emerging technologies and teaching methodologies

Introduction:
In today's rapidly evolving world, environmental education has become more important than ever before. As students, you play a crucial role in shaping the future of our planet. Understanding the importance of education in environmental stewardship is key to creating a sustainable future. In this subchapter, we will explore the exciting advancements in environmental education, focusing on emerging technologies and teaching methodologies that are revolutionizing the way we learn and engage with environmental issues.

1. Harnessing the Power of Technology:
One of the most significant innovations in environmental education is the integration of emerging technologies. Virtual reality, augmented reality, and immersive simulations allow students to experience real-life environmental scenarios, even if they are unable to physically visit certain locations. These technologies provide a unique opportunity to explore diverse ecosystems, witness the impact of human activities, and brainstorm potential solutions.

2. Gamification for Engaging Learning:
Gamification, the application of game elements in non-game contexts, is revolutionizing the way students learn about the environment. By transforming educational content into interactive games, learning becomes more engaging and enjoyable. Through gamification,

students can solve environmental challenges, make critical decisions, and witness the consequences of their actions in a safe virtual environment. This approach fosters a sense of responsibility and empowers students to become active environmental stewards.

3. Project-Based Learning:
Project-based learning is gaining popularity as an effective teaching methodology in environmental education. This approach encourages students to actively engage in real-world projects, such as designing sustainable solutions, conducting research, or creating environmental awareness campaigns. By working on these projects, students develop critical thinking, problem-solving, and collaboration skills, while also gaining a deeper understanding of environmental issues.

4. Online Learning Platforms:
The rise of online learning platforms has made quality environmental education accessible to a wider audience. These platforms offer a variety of courses, webinars, and resources on environmental topics, allowing students to learn at their own pace and convenience. Furthermore, online platforms often foster global collaboration and networking, enabling students to connect with like-minded individuals from different backgrounds and cultures.

Conclusion:
As students, understanding the importance of education in environmental stewardship is crucial for building a sustainable future. By exploring emerging technologies and teaching methodologies in environmental education, you can enhance your learning experience and become empowered to make a positive impact. Embrace these innovations, harness the power of knowledge, and together, we can

inspire environmental stewardship and create a better world for generations to come.

Advocating for Environmental Education: Encouraging policymakers and stakeholders to prioritize environmental education in educational systems

In today's rapidly changing world, environmental issues and concerns have become more prevalent than ever before. As young students, you have the power and responsibility to shape the future and make a positive impact on our planet. One of the most effective ways to do so is through education. By advocating for environmental education, we can ensure that policymakers and stakeholders prioritize this crucial subject in educational systems worldwide.

Environmental education is not just about learning facts and figures; it is about fostering a deep understanding of our interconnectedness with the natural world and inspiring a sense of stewardship. Through environmental education, students gain the knowledge and skills necessary to address complex environmental challenges such as climate change, deforestation, and pollution. It equips them with the tools to become informed decision-makers and responsible citizens who can contribute to a sustainable future.

To advocate for environmental education, it is essential to engage and mobilize policymakers and stakeholders. Policymakers play a significant role in shaping educational systems and allocating resources. By highlighting the importance of environmental education, its positive impact on student learning outcomes, and its relevance to the pressing environmental issues we face today, we can encourage policymakers to allocate more resources and curriculum time to this subject.

Additionally, engaging stakeholders such as teachers, parents, and community leaders is crucial. They have a direct influence on educational practices and can play a vital role in integrating environmental education into the curriculum. By raising awareness about the benefits of environmental education, fostering partnerships with environmental organizations, and providing professional development opportunities for educators, stakeholders can actively contribute to the promotion of environmental education.

It is important to emphasize the interdisciplinary nature of environmental education. Environmental issues do not exist in isolation but intersect with various subjects such as science, social studies, and even the arts. By integrating environmental education across different disciplines, we can provide students with a holistic and comprehensive understanding of the environment and its challenges. This interdisciplinary approach also fosters critical thinking, problem-solving, and creativity, skills that are essential for addressing complex environmental problems.

As students, your voices matter. By advocating for environmental education, you can create a ripple effect that extends beyond the classroom. Start by educating yourself about environmental issues and the benefits of environmental education. Join or form student organizations that focus on environmental sustainability. Write letters, organize events, and engage in dialogue with policymakers and stakeholders. Your passion and dedication can inspire others and create meaningful change.

Together, let us advocate for environmental education and ensure that it becomes a priority in educational systems worldwide. By equipping future generations with the knowledge, skills, and values necessary to protect and sustain our planet, we can create a more sustainable and thriving world for all.

Creating a Sustainable World: Discussing the potential long-term impact of widespread environmental education on global sustainability

Education has always been a powerful tool for change, shaping minds and inspiring action. In today's world, where environmental challenges are becoming more pressing by the day, it is crucial for students to understand the importance of environmental stewardship. This subchapter explores the potential long-term impact of widespread environmental education on global sustainability, highlighting why education holds the key to creating a sustainable world.

At its core, environmental education aims to raise awareness and deepen understanding of the interconnectedness between humans and the natural world. By equipping students with knowledge about environmental issues, such as climate change, deforestation, and pollution, they gain the ability to critically analyze these challenges and make informed decisions. This knowledge empowers them to become active contributors to a sustainable future.

One of the most significant long-term impacts of widespread environmental education is the cultivation of a generation of environmentally conscious individuals. As students learn about the consequences of unsustainable practices, they become more aware of their own actions and the impact they have on the environment. This awareness can lead to changes in lifestyle choices, such as adopting sustainable consumption patterns, reducing waste, and advocating for renewable energy sources. By internalizing the principles of environmental stewardship, students can become agents of change within their communities, inspiring others to follow suit.

Moreover, environmental education fosters a sense of responsibility and connection to nature. By learning about the intricate web of life and the delicate balance of ecosystems, students develop a deep appreciation for the natural world. This emotional connection fuels a desire to protect and conserve nature, making them more likely to engage in sustainable practices throughout their lives.

In addition to individual actions, widespread environmental education can drive systemic change. As students become more knowledgeable about environmental issues, they can use their voices to advocate for policy changes and demand sustainable practices from governments and businesses. This collective action has the potential to transform industries, promote renewable energy, and drive innovation towards a greener future.

In conclusion, the potential long-term impact of widespread environmental education on global sustainability is immense. By equipping students with knowledge, fostering a sense of responsibility, and empowering them to take action, education can inspire a generation of environmentally conscious individuals. From personal choices to systemic change, education holds the power to create a sustainable world. As students, embracing the importance of education in environmental stewardship can shape our future and pave the way for a healthier, more sustainable planet.

Conclusion: The Power of Knowledge in Environmental Stewardship

In our journey through "The Power of Knowledge: How Education Inspires Environmental Stewardship," we have explored the profound impact that education can have on our understanding and commitment to environmental stewardship. As students, you hold the key to unlocking a future that is sustainable, responsible, and environmentally conscious. The importance of education in this regard cannot be overstated.

Throughout this book, we have seen how education empowers individuals to make informed choices and take action to protect our planet. By equipping ourselves with knowledge about the environment, we gain a deeper understanding of the intricate web of life and the interconnectedness of all living things. This knowledge helps us appreciate the fragility and beauty of nature, instilling a sense of responsibility to preserve it for future generations.

Education provides us with the tools to critically analyze environmental issues and seek innovative solutions. It encourages us to think creatively, fostering a mindset that embraces sustainability and eco-friendly practices. Through education, we can challenge the status quo and advocate for policies and practices that promote environmental conservation.

Furthermore, education helps us develop a sense of empathy towards all living beings. By learning about the impact of our actions on the environment, we become more compassionate and mindful of our choices. We recognize that our individual actions, no matter how small, can contribute to the greater good of the planet.

As students, you have a unique opportunity to harness the power of knowledge and drive positive change. By pursuing education, you not only enhance your own understanding but also inspire others to join the cause of environmental stewardship. You are the future leaders, scientists, policymakers, and innovators who will shape the world we live in.

Remember, the journey towards environmental stewardship is a lifelong commitment. It requires continuous learning, growth, and adaptation. Embrace education as a lifelong pursuit and seek out opportunities to expand your knowledge about the environment. Engage in discussions, participate in community initiatives, and explore interdisciplinary approaches to environmental issues.

In conclusion, the power of knowledge in environmental stewardship is immense. Education equips us with the understanding, skills, and empathy necessary to make a positive impact on our planet. As students, it is your responsibility to embrace the importance of education and use it as a catalyst for change. Together, we can create a future where environmental sustainability is not just an aspiration, but a reality.

Reiterating the importance of education in inspiring environmental stewardship and summarizing key takeaways from the book.

Reiterating the Importance of Education in Inspiring Environmental Stewardship and Summarizing Key Takeaways from the Book

Education has always been a powerful tool for shaping the future of our planet. In today's world, where environmental challenges are growing at an alarming rate, the role of education in inspiring environmental stewardship has become more crucial than ever. The book, "The Power of Knowledge: How Education Inspires Environmental Stewardship," delves into the profound impact education can have on individuals and society as a whole.

Throughout the chapters, the book highlights the importance of education in fostering a sense of responsibility towards the environment. It emphasizes that education is not just about acquiring knowledge but also about understanding the interconnectedness of our actions with the natural world. By providing students with a comprehensive understanding of environmental issues, education empowers them to make informed decisions and take actions that contribute to a more sustainable future.

One of the key takeaways from the book is that education plays a vital role in shaping sustainable attitudes and behaviors. By instilling a sense of environmental consciousness from an early age, education lays the foundation for a generation of environmentally responsible citizens. From teaching the importance of recycling and conserving resources to promoting renewable energy solutions, education equips students with the knowledge and skills needed to become effective environmental stewards.

Another important aspect highlighted in the book is the role of education in promoting innovation and finding solutions to environmental challenges. By nurturing critical thinking, problem-solving, and creativity, education empowers students to develop innovative approaches to address complex environmental problems. The book showcases inspiring examples of young individuals who have used their education to make a significant impact in environmental conservation, proving that education holds the key to unlocking our collective potential for positive change.

In conclusion, "The Power of Knowledge: How Education Inspires Environmental Stewardship" underscores the immense importance of education in inspiring environmental stewardship. By providing students with a holistic understanding of environmental issues, education cultivates a sense of responsibility, promotes sustainable attitudes and behaviors, and nurtures innovation. As students, we have the power to harness the knowledge gained through education to become the environmental stewards our planet needs. Let us embrace the transformative power of education and work towards creating a greener, more sustainable future for ourselves and generations to come.